Investigate the Possibilities

Elementary Physics

ENERGY

Its Forms, Changes, & Functions

Student Journal

Tom DeRosa
Carolyn Reeves

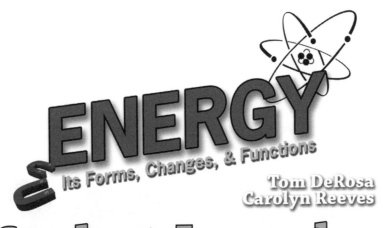

ENERGY
Its Forms, Changes, & Functions

Tom DeRosa
Carolyn Reeves

Student Journal

First Printing: August 2009

Master Books®
P.O. Box 726
Green Forest, AR 72638

Printed in the United States of America

Cover Design by Diana Bogardus
Interior Design by Terry White

ISBN 10: 0-89051-571-9
ISBN 13: 978-0-89051-571-6

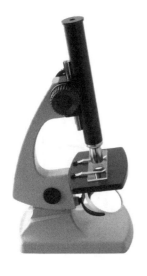

Investigate the Possibilities

All Scripture references are New International Version unless otherwise noted.

All images from shutterstock.com

Please visit our website for other great titles: www.masterbooks.net

Table of Contents

Note to the Student

...cord your ideas, questions, observations, and answers in the student book. Begin with "Think-...g about This." After you read "Think about This," try to recall and note any experiences you have ...d related to the topic, or make notes of what you would like to learn.

...cord all observations and data obtained from each activity.

...u should do at least one Dig Deeper project each week. Your teacher will tell you how many ...ojects you are required to do, but feel free to do more if you find an area that is especially ...teresting to you. The reason for the large number of projects is to give you choices. This allows ...u to dig deeper into those areas you are most interested in pursuing. Most of these projects ...ll need to be turned in separately from the Student Answer Book, but uses the Student Answer ...ok to record the projects you choose to do along with a brief summary of each project and the ...te each is completed.

Record the answers to "What Did You Learn."

The Stumper's Corner is your time to ask the questions. Write two short-answer questions related to each lesson that are hard enough to stump someone. Write your questions along with the correct answer or write two questions that you don't know and would like to know more about.

Some of these experiments should be done with the help of adult supervision. They have been specifically designed for educational purposes, with materials that are readily available.

Investigation #1
Where Exactly Does Energy Go?

Date:

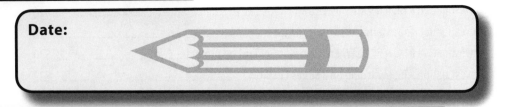

The Activity:
Procedure and Observations

1. Make a drawing to show how you connected the lightbulb, a wire, and a battery to make the light come on.

Drawing Board:

2. Could you tell that the lightbulb was warmer after it was turned on?

_____

3. Feel the sandpaper and the board after you have rubbed them together. What kind of energy is produced?

_____

4. Pluck the rubber bands. Can you see that they are vibrating?

_____

Can you hear the sound they make while they are vibrating?

_____

Compare the pitch made by the different rubber bands.

_____

1. Give two examples of how one form of energy can change into heat energy. Give another example of an energy change.

   _____

   _____

2. List two ways in which energy does work for us.

   _____

   _____

3. The following list contains examples of forces, properties of matter, and forms of energy. Underline all the examples of forms of energy: inertia, light, heat, density, buoyancy, electricity, lift, weight, chemical, push, nuclear.

4. Define mechanical energy and give an example.

   _____

   _____

5. What kind of energy can be quickly provided by a battery?

   _____

6. What is the law of conservation of energy?

   _____

   _____

7. Give an example of when an unwanted form of energy is produced in a device. _____

8. What happens to a roomful of light on a dark night when the lights are turned off? _____

9. Was energy transferred from the battery to the lightbulb when an electric circuit was completed? _____

1. _____

   _____

2. _____

   _____

Date:

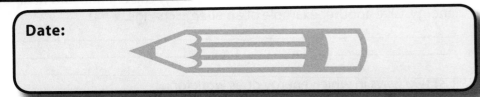

The Activity: Procedure and Observations

When you first released the marble from the top of the track, did it have enough energy to make it over the hill? _____

When you made the hill taller than the beginning of the track, did the marble have enough energy to make it over the hill? _____

Were you able to increase the height of the starting place so that the marble made it over the hill? _____

Make drawings of two designs that worked and one design that didn't work. Measure and include the heights of your hills and the starting positions in your drawings.

Drawing Board:

Design and construct a track for the marble that includes hills, valleys, and curves. Did the marble make it all the way to the end of the track?

_____

Make a list of the curves, hills, and other features where the marble stopped or jumped the track. Try to think of a reason why it did this in each instance.

_____   _____
_____   _____
_____   _____

If the marble didn't make it around the track or you simply wanted to make it more exciting, did you adjust or redesign your track? _____

Did the marble make it to the end of the track after you made adjustments? _____

Make a drawing or diagram of your final track.

Drawing Board:

What Did You Learn ?

1. Give two examples of energy that is stored in such a way that it can be used at a later time.

   _____
   _____

2. Does a tank full of gasoline contain potential or kinetic energy?

   _____

3. At what point on a roller coaster ride is the potential energy the greatest? _____

4. At what point on a roller coaster ride is the kinetic energy the greatest? _____

5. How can an archer increase the potential energy of an arrow that is about to be shot?

   _____
   _____

6. Which form of energy is more powerful — nuclear or chemical?

   _____

7. How can a marble be given more potential energy at the beginning of the track? _____

8. What force prevented the marble from rolling a little higher than it did? _____

✎ Stumper's Corner

1. _____
   _____
   _____

2. _____
   _____
   _____

What would happen to our cars and air conditioners if fuel supplies were used up?

To **Dig Deeper** about this important problem, see if you can find more information about what is being done to be wise stewards of our natural coal, oil, and gas resources or to find new ways to make our cars, heaters, and air conditioners work. You can summarize several ideas or concentrate on just one idea.

Date:

The Activity: Procedure and Observations

1. Set up a flat mirror so that you are looking in the mirror at an angle. Were you able to see your partner in the mirror? _____

2. What does your partner see at the same time you see him or her?
   _____

3. Change your position so that you can still see the mirror, but not yourself. Estimate where your partner will have to be in order for you to see him/her in the mirror.
   _____
   _____
   _____

4. Make a diagram of you, the mirror, and your partner. Show the path of a beam of light coming from your partner to the mirror to your eyes.

Drawing Board:

5. Sit with your back to a window and hold a flat mirror in front of you. Take a second mirror and hold it above the first one at an angle that lets you see outside the window. Describe what you see.
   _____
   _____
   _____
   _____

6. Find a highly polished tablespoon. Look at yourself using the inside of the spoon. Move the spoon back and forth. What kind of images do you see at different distances?
   _____
   _____

7. Look at yourself using the back of the spoon. How do you look?
   _____
   _____
   _____

8. Take a piece of white paper and make a 1-cm black circle with your pencil on the paper. Go outside and use a convex lens to focus sunlight on the white paper. Note what happens.
   _____
   _____
   _____

9. Now use a convex lens to focus sunlight on the black circle. Note what happens. **Do not look directly at the bright light produced by the lens.** Write an explanation for your observations.
   _____
   _____
   _____

mirror

window

mirror

beam of light

Light travels in a straight line and is reflected each time it hits a mirror. This is how a periscope works.

1. When light is absorbed by an object, what form of energy will much of it eventually change into? _____

2. If a beam of light strikes a flat mirror at a 45° angle, at what angle will it be reflected off the mirror? _____

3. What happens when light hits a white object? _____
_____

4. What happens when light hits a black object? _____
_____

5. Explain why white clothes are cooler in the summer than black clothes. _____

6. Do mirrors that are curved toward you magnify things or make them appear smaller? _____

7. What are three things that can happen to a beam of light that hits an object? _____
_____
_____

8. Why are convex mirrors used in side-installed rear view car mirrors? _____

Dig Deeper

Stumper's Corner

1. _____
_____

2. _____
_____

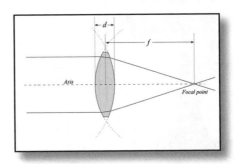

Date:

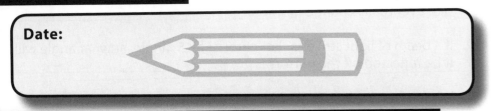

The Activity:
Procedure and Observations

1. As your partner poured water into the bowl, did the penny become visible? _____

2. When you observed a pencil out of a glass of water, describe how it looked from different angles.
_____
_____
_____

3. Place a convex lens near your eye, and look through it at an object that is at least 5 meters away. Describe how the object looks.
_____
_____
_____

4. Slowly move the lens farther away from your eye as you continue to look at the object through the lens. Does the object look larger or smaller as you move the lens farther away? _____

5. Continue to move the lens farther away from the object. Is there a point where you can't see it because it is too blurry? _____

6. Continue to move the lens farther away from the picture. Is there a point where the object looks upside-down? _____
Does the size of the object look smaller or larger? _____

7. Continue to look through the lens at your object with your arm fully extended. Now take another convex lens and hold it near your eye. Look through both lenses at the same time until you see a focused image. Describe the focused image.
_____
_____
_____

1. Are the frames for a film that goes into a movie projector upside-down or right side up? _____

2. Label the parts of the human eye: pupil, convex lens, retina. Where does an image focus inside the eye?

3. When an image focuses inside the eye, is it right side up or upside-down? _____ What part of our body is necessary to interpret this image? _____

4. What equipment is needed to make a simple telescope?
   _____

5. What equipment is needed to make a simple microscope?
   _____

6. Compare telescopes and microscopes. Give two ways they are similar.
   _____
   _____

7. Where is a convex lens the thickest and where is it the thinnest?
   _____

8. As light travels through the air, does it go in a straight line? _____

9. What happens to a beam of light when it leaves the air and enters a glass of water? _____

Stumper's Corner ✏️

1. _____
   _____
   _____

2. _____
   _____

Galileo Takes on Aristotle

Why did the Church leaders try to protect Aristotle's teachings about science? _____
Do you think this was a wise thing for the Church to do? _____

Investigation #5

Waving the Red, Green, and Blue

Date:

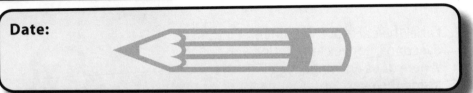

The Activity: Procedure and Observations

1. What color do you see when the spinner is turning rapidly?

   _____

2. Use your prism to find a spectrum of rainbow colors. Name the colors your see in order, starting with red, which has the longest wavelength of visible light. Some people use the name ROY G. BIV to help them remember these colors. (Actually, indigo is the same as violet, so just name 6 colors.)

   1. _____   4. _____
   2. _____   5. _____
   3. _____   6. _____

3. When you hold a stretched-out slinky and move your hand quickly to the right and then back to the left you will observe that a pulse moves from your hand to your partner. Does it bounce back when it reaches your partner? _____

4. Describe the direction of the movement of a piece of tape on one of the coils.

   _____

   _____

5. Place a piece of tape on one of the slinky coils and observe the direction it moves as you make more waves. If you can move your hand at the right speed, you will see smooth, regular waves. Record your observations or make a drawing of how they look.

   _____

   _____

Dig Deeper

1. What are the three primary colors of light?
    1. _____
    2. _____
    3. _____

2. Are these the same as the primary colors of paint? _____

3. What color would you see if equal amounts of the three primary colors of light were shined together on a screen? _____

4. What is a triangular-shaped piece of glass or plastic that separates the colors of light into the visible spectrum? _____

5. Of the visible colors of light, which has the longest wavelength? _____ Which has the shortest wavelength? _____

6. Explain the diagram. Tell which waves are absorbed and which one is reflected.
    _____
    _____

ROY G BIV

Red object

7. Invisible light waves that are a little longer than red and can be felt as heat waves are called what? _____
_____

8. When light hits a black object, are all the colors reflected or absorbed? _____

1. _____
_____

2. _____
_____

9. What happens to light waves that are absorbed by an object?
_____

10. When you stretch out a slinky between two people and shake the end of the slinky from side to side, what kind of wave do you see traveling through the slinky? _____

11. Give five examples of transverse waves.
    1. _____   4. _____
    2. _____   5. _____
    3. _____

12. Can transverse waves travel through space as well as through air?
_____

13. Do waves carry energy? _____

14. Do different colors of light have different wavelengths? _____

What do you think pure white symbolizes?
_____
_____
_____

What do you think darkness symbolizes?
_____
_____
_____

Did You Hear That?

 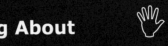
Date:

Slinkies showing compression and expansion

The Activity:
Procedure and Observations

1. Place your fingertips on your neck near where you think your voice box is located and gently exhale. Now gently hum a low note as you exhale. Can you feel a difference when you hum?_____

2. Pluck a rubber band where one end is being held in your teeth. Can you tell that it is vibrating? _____ Is there a sound being made by the rubber band? _____

3. If you have a tuning fork, your teacher will demonstrate how a vibrating tuning fork will effect the water in a glass. What happens to the water? _____ What does a vibrating tuning fork do to a piece of paper?_____

4. Hold one end of a rubber band in your teeth and stretch the band. Pluck the band. Can you tell that it is vibrating? _____ Is there a sound being made by the rubber band? _____

5. Find the box you made for activity #1. You have already noted that the thinnest rubber band produced the highest pitch. Place a block on the bottom of the box and slip the rubber bands over it to increase the tension. Pluck the bands again. Did the pitch change?
_____

6. Hold the metal slinky between you and your partner like you did in the lesson on light. This time you will make a wave known as a longitudinal wave. Quickly push forward and then pull back on the slinky with your hand. Place a piece of tape on one of the coils. Describe how the tape moves as you make a longitudinal wave. Recall how a piece of tape moved as you made a transverse wave. Compare the movement of the piece of tape in both longitudinal waves and transverse waves.
_____
_____

7. Do you see a pulse move from your hand to your partner? _____ Does it bounce back? _____

8. Try to time your movement so waves going out and the waves bouncing back meet in rhythm. Do you see alternating areas where the coils are close together and far apart? _____

9. Compare the movements of the piece of tape of longitudinal waves and transverse waves.
_____

1. Light waves are what kind of wave? _____

2. Sound waves are what kind of wave? _____

3. Why are there no sounds on the moon?_____
_____

4. Are all sounds made by vibrating objects? _____

5. Suppose you notice a guitar has a thick string and a thin string that seem to be the same length and have the same tension. Which string would have the highest pitch? _____

6. What are three ways in which one sound differs from another?
   1. _____
   2. _____
   3. _____

7. Suppose you stretch out a slinky between two people and push and pull one end of the slinky as your partner holds the other end. What kind of wave do you see traveling through the slinky? _____

8. What tends to be the difference when sound waves hit a hard surface and when they hit a soft surface?
_____
_____

Stumper's Corner 🖉

1. _____
_____

2. _____
_____

Investigation #7
When Things Get Hot

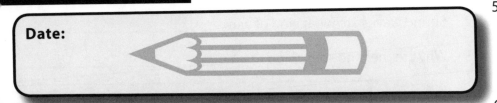

Date:

The Activity:
Procedure and Observations

1. Add a drop of food coloring to a glass of cold water and another drop to a glass of hot water. Observe the glasses for a few minutes. Record your observations.

   _____
   _____
   _____
   _____

2. Check the glasses every five minutes throughout the rest of the class or until the food coloring is evenly distributed throughout the water. Record observations each time you check the glasses.

   _____
   _____
   _____
   _____
   _____

3. Wear safety glasses. Begin to heat one end of a metal rod in a candle flame as you hold the rod at the other end. Note the time it takes for the heat to travel from the flame to your hand. **(Remember, only do procedures involving fire and heat with adult supervision.)**

4. After removing the rod from the flame, put on an oven mitt. Hold the rod with the mitt as you continue to heat the rod for another minute. Do you feel the heat now? _____

5. Mark the level of the water in the tube. Put your hands around the flask to warm it. What happens to the level of the water in the tube as you put your hands around the flask to warm it?

   _____
   _____

6. What happens to the level of the water in the tube as you rub the flask with a piece of ice?

   _____
   _____

7. Try to give an explanation for what you see.

   _____
   _____

8. What is the temperature of the air around you according to your thermometer? _____

9. Predict the temperature of the air in four other locations. Record your predictions and then measure the temperature of the air in each place. Record your readings.

   Ceiling —
   Floor —
   Window —
   Other —

1. _____
   _____

2. _____
   _____

What Did You Learn ?

1. Write a definition of heat.
   _____
   _____

2. What kind of substances allow heat to travel through them easily?
   _____

3. A water molecule is made up of which two kinds of atoms?
   _____

4. Does the liquid in a thermometer expand or contract when it gets hotter? _____

5. What happens to the motion of the molecules of a liquid when the liquid gets hotter? _____

6. Why do bridge engineers have to design ways for the materials in the bridge to be able to expand and contract?
   _____

7. Why could you feel the heat in the metal rod with your bare hand, but you couldn't feel heat from the rod when you were wearing the kitchen mitt? _____

8. Give an explanation for why telephone wires that are strung in the summer are allowed to sag a little rather than being pulled tight.
   _____
   _____

Dig Deeper ✏

9. What is the difference in transferring heat energy by conduction and by convection?
   _____
   _____

10. If the temperature outside is 40°C, would you need to wear a warm winter coat or a summer outfit? _____

Conducting a Controlled Experiment

Design and build a box to insulate a piece of ice. What kind of box was the best insulator for a piece of ice? _____

What are the controls in this experiment? _____

What is the variable in this experiment? _____

What are some ways to study science other than by doing controlled experiments? _____

Is all scientific research conducted by doing controlled experiments ?

Do all scientific investigators use the same methods? _____

What is the main difference in science and technology?
_____

Is there someone you have seen on TV or in the news who would fit the description of a quasi-scientist or an impostor? _____
What would make you think this? _____

In what ways is Reco different from his brothers and sisters?
_____

Reco's brothers and sisters always look for natural explanations in their research. Why is it difficult for Reco to find an all-natural explanation for where every living or once-living organism came from?
_____

Date:

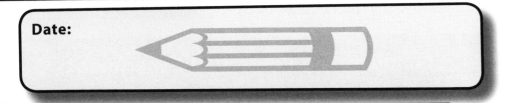

The Activity:
Procedure and Observations

1. Fill a 12-oz cup one-third full with hot water. Fill the other 12-oz cup one-third full with cold water. Measure the temperature of the water in each cup.

2. Now pour the hot water into the cold water to make warm water. Measure the temperature of this water, using the calorimeter.

3. What is the difference between the temperature of the hot water and the warm water (last temperature reading)?

   _____
   _____
   _____

4. What is the difference between the warm water (last temperature reading) and the temperature of the cold water?

   _____
   _____
   _____

5. Try to come up with your own explanation for why the hot water got colder and the cold water got hotter. Don't simply say they mixed.

What Did You Learn ?

1. On a cold day, does a well-insulated house keep the cold out or does it keep the heat inside? _____

2. Give three ways in which heat can be transferred from one object to another.
    1. _____
    2. _____
    3. _____

3. Explain what causes sea breezes. Do they occur during the day or at night?
    _____
    _____
    _____
    _____

4. What are two units used to measure heat energy?
    1. _____
    2. _____

5. How does the sun's energy reach the earth?
    _____
    _____
    _____

6. Does warm air tend to rise or sink? _____

7. When a hot object is next to a cold object, how does heat always move? _____

Stumper's Corner

1. _____
    _____
2. _____
    _____

Investigation #9
Magnets are Very Attractive

Date:

The Activity:
Procedure and Observations

Fill in the chart below.

Things a magnet attracts	Things a magnet does not attract

Are all metals attracted to a magnet? _____

Are there any nonmetals that were attracted to a magnet? _____

Pass the various items on the tray between the magnet and the paper clip. Record which materials allow the magnetic field to pass through and which do not.

Things that pass through a magnetic field	Things that do not pass through a magnetic field

According to your observations, which materials would allow the magnetic field to pass through them?

_____

_____

Which did not?

_____

_____

Compare the two charts. How are they alike?

_____

_____

An electromagnet has been assembled by the teacher. See if it will attract the same materials the other magnet did. (Disconnect a wire in between tests and work fast.)
Try to pick up several iron washers with the electromagnet. While they are suspended, disconnect one of the wires to the battery. What happens? _____

1. Will a magnet pick up a copper penny? _____

2. Will a magnet pick up an iron nail? _____

3. If you put a sheet of aluminum under a magnet, will you prevent the magnetic force from going through it? _____

4. Which of the following materials are magnetic materials: glass, steel, nickel, wood, water, gold, cobalt, magnesium, oxygen, iron, plastic?

5. Which of the materials listed in #4 could a magnetic field pass through?

   _____

   _____

6. How are regular magnets and electromagnets alike?

   _____

   _____

7. How are regular magnets and electromagnets different?

   _____

   _____

Stumper's Corner 🖉

1. _____

   _____

8. What is lodestone?

2. _____

   _____

   _____

Investigation #10
Magnetism is Pretty Special

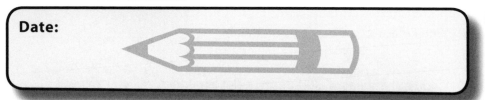

Date:

The Activity:
Procedure and Observations

Bring the S (south) end of another magnet toward the S end of the hanging magnet. Bring the N (north) end toward the N end of the hanging magnet. Now bring the N (north) end of the magnet toward the S end of the hanging magnet. This time bring the S end of the magnet toward the N end of the hanging magnet. Record what happens each time:

S toward S —

N toward N —

N toward S —

S toward N —

Cause the magnet to stop moving. Spin it slightly and allow it to come to a complete stop on its own. Repeat several times and record which way the magnet points when it stops.

_____

_____

Place a compass on the table in front of you. Compare the direction the needle in the compass points with the direction of the hanging magnet when it stops moving.

_____

_____

Repeat the demonstration you saw at the beginning of the class, but this time measure the distance between the magnets when you first see the hanging magnet start to move. Which magnet causes the hanging magnet to turn from the greatest distance? _____

Do both magnets affect the hanging magnet from the same distance?

_____

Lay a centimeter ruler on the table and place a pin at the end of the ruler. Slowly slide a magnet from the other end of the ruler. Record the distance between the magnet and the pin when the pin first moves.

_____

_____

Repeat the activity with another magnet. Determine which of the magnets is the most powerful (has the strongest force) by how far away it is from the pin when the pin moves. _____

Predict what will happen when you place the N end of one magnet near the center of the other magnet? Try it and see what happens.

_____

_____

You probably can tell just from feeling the effects that the magnetic forces get stronger the closer you hold two magnetic poles together. Try to push two like poles closer together with your hands. Record how it feels.

_____

_____

Now try to hold two opposite poles apart with a small space between the poles. Record how it feels.

_____
_____
_____

1. Under what conditions will two bar magnets push away from each other even when they are not touching?

   _____
   _____

2. Under what conditions will two bar magnets pull on each other even when they are not touching?

   _____
   _____

3. In what direction does a bar magnet that is suspended on a string point when it stops moving? _____

4. In what direction does a compass needle point when it stops moving? _____

5. Which end of a freely turning magnet points north? _____

6. What is one way to measure the strength of a magnet?

   _____

7. Is the north pole of a freely turning magnet attracted to the earth's Geographic North Pole or the Magnetic North Pole?

   _____

Dig Deeper 🖉

Stumper's Corner 🖉

1. _____
   _____

2. _____
   _____

Investigation #11
How Do Magnets Become Magnets?

Date:

The Activity:
Procedure and Observations

What does the compass needle do when it is placed next to the tube of iron filings?

_____

_____

What does the compass needle do after the tube has been rubbed with a strong magnet?

_____

_____

What does the compass needle do after the tube has been shaken?

_____

_____

Remove the iron filings and replace them with small cut up pieces of aluminum. Repeat the experiment the same way you did with the tube of iron filings. Tell how the compass behaved each time.

_____

_____

Take a large steel paper clip and straighten it. Touch it to a small steel paper clip. What happens?

_____

_____

Rub a straightened clip with a magnet. Now touch the straightened clip to some small paper clips. What happens?

_____

_____

Tap the straightened clip on a hard surface several times. Touch it to the small paper clips again. What happens?

_____

_____

Dig Deeper

1. What do magnetic materials have in them that other materials do not have? _____

2. Name something that is a magnetic material and name something that is not a magnetic material. _____

3. Can a bar of copper be made into a magnet? _____
   Why or why not? _____

4. What is the difference in how the domains are arranged in a magnetic material that is not magnetized and in a magnet? (A diagram is a good way to answer this.)

5. Why can things like wood, lead, tin, or plastic materials not be made into magnets? _____

6. Can a magnetic material that is not magnetized become magnetized? _____ Explain _____

7. How might you cause a magnet to lose its strength?
   _____

8. Why would a manufacturer of magnets not guarantee them if you drop them?
   _____

Stumper's Corner

1. _____

2. _____

Writing Project: The Rescue

Treat this project the same as a "Dig Deeper" project.

Date:

The Activity:
Procedure and Observations

After you have arranged the magnet, pieces of wood, and paper, carefully sprinkle the iron filings on the paper, over and around where the magnet rests. What do the iron filings do as you very gently tap the edge of the paper? _____

Make a drawing of the pattern you observe.

Drawing Board:

How does a compass needle turn when it is held near the north pole of the magnet? _____

How does a compass needle turn when it is held near the south pole of the magnet? _____

How does a compass needle turn when it is held at various other places?

_____

Place two magnets about two cm apart with north poles facing. Make a drawing of the pattern you observe as you sprinkle iron filings over the paper and gently tap the paper.

Drawing Board:

This time, place two magnets about two cm apart with a north pole and a south pole facing each other. After you have sprinkled iron filings over the paper and tapped the paper, make a drawing of the pattern you observe.

Drawing Board:

Place a magnet in a thin, covered box and tape it in place. Using only your compass, see if you can accurately identify where the magnet is located, as well as which end is the N pole and which is the S pole. Fold a piece of paper to be the size of the box top and draw how you think the magnet is placed.

An electromagnet has been assembled by the teacher, and iron filings have been sprinkled over it in the same way the first activities were conducted. Tap the paper gently until you can see a pattern. Do the patterns made by a permanent magnet and an electromagnet look similar? _____

How does a compass behave near the electromagnet?

_____

1. What is a compass needle?
_____

2. On what did the iron filings become aligned when you sprinkled them over a magnet? _____

3. A magnetic line of force extends from what to what?
_____

4. Does the earth have magnetic lines of force that go from the earth's Magnetic North Pole to the earth's Magnetic South Pole?
_____

5. Explain how the earth's magnetic field protects us from many of the harmful radiations that come from the sun.
_____
_____
_____
_____

6. Where are the magnetic lines of force around a magnet closest together? _____

7. What do scientists believe causes the earth to have a magnetic field?
_____

8. How would you describe the interaction of magnetic poles?
_____
_____

9. Is there a magnetic field around a magnet? _____

10. Is there a magnetic field around a moving current of electricity?
_____

Stumper's Corner ✏

1. _____
_____

2. _____
_____

Thinking About

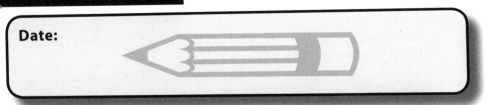

Date:

The Activity:
Procedure and Observations

What did the two strips of plastic do when you picked them up and held them close together without touching?

_____
_____
_____

What did the two strips of plastic do after you rubbed them with the wool cloth and held them close together but not touching?

_____
_____
_____

Vigorously rub the comb with the wool cloth. What happens to the charged comb when it is held close to the rice cereal for a few minutes?

_____
_____
_____

Hang two inflated balloons so they are about two or three centimeters apart. What did the balloons do?

_____
_____
_____

What happens after you rub the balloons with the wool cloth?

_____
_____
_____

What happens after you rub a glass jar with a nylon cloth and bring it near the balloons?

_____
_____
_____

 Stumper's Corner

1. _____
   _____

2. _____
   _____

Dig Deeper ✏️

Pause and Think: Lightning Safety

Where are some places you should not to be during a thunderstorm?

_____

_____

_____

What Did You Learn ❓

1. Suppose you feel a little shock after walking across a carpeted floor and touching a metal door handle. Is this kind of shock caused by current electricity or static electricity? _____

2. Did protons, neutrons, or electrons move between your hand and the metal door handle to cause the shock? _____

3. Atoms contain positive, negative, and neutral particles. Which two kinds of particles are found in the nucleus of an atom?
   1. _____
   2. _____

4. What do you call the space around an object with a positive or negative static charge? _____

5. What kind of field is around a moving electric current? _____
   _____

6. Do electrons have a positive or a negative charge? _____

7. What happens when two negatively charged balloons come near each other? _____

8. What happens when a positively charged balloon comes near a negatively charged glass? _____

9. What happens when a negatively charged comb comes near a neutral piece of rice cereal?
   _____

A Place Where Electrons Get Pushed Around

Date:

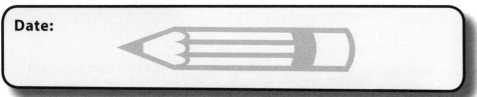

The Activity:
Procedure and Observations

First, make a simple electroscope from the directions given. To see how it works, use a piece of wool to rub the comb. This will cause the comb to acquire an electric charge. Slowly move the comb until it touches the top of the wire. What happens to the piece of foil when a charged comb touches the wire?

_____

_____

_____

Discharge the electroscope by touching the top of the wire. Charge the comb again and move it near the top of the wire, but don't let them touch. What happens to the piece of foil when a charged comb is brought near the copper wire?

_____

_____

_____

Test the following objects by bringing them close to the wire coil: a wooden pencil, a green leaf, and a glass cup. Record what the two aluminum foil pieces do.

_____

_____

_____

Try charging some objects by rubbing them with another material. Things like rubber, paper, and plastic objects tend to hold a charge. Wool, nylon, and silk are likely to produce a charge on these objects. Try charging a variety of objects. Bring each object near the wire coil. Keep up with how you charged each object you tested. Record what happened each time.

_____

_____

_____

Dig Deeper

What Did You Learn ?

1. Explain what might cause some of the electrons to get pushed down to the foil in the electroscope and make the foil move apart.
   _____

2. Explain what might cause some of the electrons to get pulled up from the foil in the electroscope and make the foil move apart.
   _____

3. Can an electron be pushed or pulled by the electric field around a charged object even though the object is not touching the electron?
   _____

4. What do we call materials that electrons can move through easily? Give two examples.
   1. _____
   2. _____

5. What do we call materials that electrons cannot move through easily? Give two examples.
   1. _____
   2. _____

6. How do you discharge an electroscope? _____

7. What are some ways in which magnets and objects with an electric charge around them are alike?
   _____

Stumper's Corner

1. _____
   _____

2. _____
   _____

How Two Simple Ideas Became Huge

Discussion:
Make a list of things you use frequently that require current electricity.
_____
_____
_____
_____
_____
_____
_____

What is an electric generator? _____
Why does it have to turn in order to produce electricity? _____

The discoveries that (1) an electric current can produce magnetism and (2) magnetism can produce an electric current are the basis for much of our technology today. Who were the scientists responsible for each of the discoveries?
_____
_____
_____
_____
_____
_____

List some of the technology we have today because of these discoveries.
_____
_____
_____
_____
_____
_____

Date:

The Activity:
Procedure and Observations

Observe the diagram of the circuit and connect your circuit in the same way. Did your lights come on? _____

If your lights didn't come on, were you able to find the problem?

_____

What happens when the switch is open?

_____

What happens when the switch is closed?

_____

What happens when you disconnect one of the wires to the bulb?

_____

What happens when you disconnect one of the wires to the battery?

_____

What happens when all the lights are on and you unscrew one of the bulbs?

_____

Take one of the bulbs and sockets out of the circuit and rewire the circuit. Is there any difference in the brightness of one bulb in the circuit and two bulbs in the circuit? _____

Draw a circuit diagram (or schematic) for a series circuit that has two cells, two lightbulbs, one switch, and five connecting wires.

Drawing Board:

Draw a circle around the source of the energy in the diagram. Draw a triangle around the things that use the energy.

Dig Deeper

1. What kind of circuit is in your house — series or parallel? _____

2. Were two bulbs wired in series just as bright as one bulb? _____

3. What is the purpose of a switch?
   _____
   _____

4. Why did removing one bulb stop the other light from coming on?
   _____
   _____

5. What four things are found in most complete circuits?
   1. _____   2. _____
   3. _____   4. _____

6. Name a few reasons why the lights might not come on after you connect everything?
   _____
   _____

7. Draw a circuit diagram of the circuit you made. Label the parts and count the wires.

8. What kind of current is produced by a battery? _____

9. What kind of current is produced by a generator and used by most household appliances? _____

10. What unwanted form of energy was produced in the lightbulb?
    _____

11. The chemical energy in the battery changed into electrical energy. What did the electrical energy change into in the lightbulb?
    _____

Stumper's Corner

1. _____
   _____

2. _____
   _____

Is a Parallel Circuit Better Than a Series Circuit

Date:

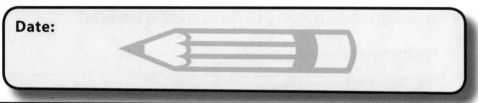

Make a circuit diagram of the circuit used in this activity.

The Activity: Procedure and Observations

Rewire the circuit that you used in the previous lesson to make a parallel circuit. What happens when all the lights are on and you unscrew one bulb?

_____

Is the remaining bulb brighter than before?

_____

What happens when you screw it back and then unscrew the other bulb?

_____

Is the remaining bulb brighter than before?

_____

What happens when you unscrew both bulbs?

_____

Explain how this parallel circuit is wired differently than the series circuit.

_____
_____
_____
_____

Drawing Board:

1. What would happen to the brightness of the lights if you added more lights to the same parallel circuit?
_____

2. Which was brighter — two lamps wired in series or two lamps wired in parallel? _____

(3–6) Refer to the following circuit diagram to answer questions 3–6.

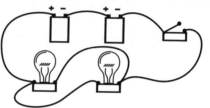

3. Are the lights wired in a series or a parallel circuit? _____

4. How many lights are shown in this circuit? _____

5. How many dry cells are shown in this circuit? _____

6. How many wires are used in this circuit? _____

7. What are two reasons why household circuits are wired in parallel?
   1. _____   2. _____

8. What is one disadvantage of connecting several lights to a battery in a parallel circuit? _____

9. As an electric generator produces electricity, connected loops of wire cut through what? _____

Stumper's Corner

1. _____
_____

2. _____
_____

Writing Project: A Summer Day in the 1800s

Write a description of how you might have spent a summer day in the 1800s. Give the name of the book you read. Who was the author? Do this assignment on other paper.

Investigation #17
The Dishwashing Liquid and Electric Current

Date:

The Activity:
Procedure and Observations

What happens when you fill your bottle with water, open the nozzle all the way, and squeeze on the bottle as hard as you can?

_____

What happens when you squeeze if the nozzle is almost completely closed, but not quite?

_____

Record what is different about the first and second squeeze.

_____

Were you able to leave the nozzle where it was and make the water come out as fast as it did the first time? _____

Describe how hard you had to push to get the water to come out faster on the third squeeze. _____

The following questions will be used to make comparisons to voltage, current, and resistance. Use the diagram to answer these questions.

Try to fill in the blanks in the chart below. Think about the bottle of water as you do this.

Relationships of current, voltage, and resistance		
Volts (How hard to push)	Resistance (Nozzle setting)	Current (Water flow)
stays same	increases (closes)	
stays same	decreases (opens)	
increases		stays same
	stays same	increases
	stays same	decreases

What happens to the current (water flow) when you decrease the voltage (push)?

_____

What happens to the current when you increase the voltage?

_____

When you change the resistance (nozzle setting) how does that affect the voltage (how hard you have to push)?

_____

What will happen to the current (water flow) if you keep the voltage (push) the same and increase the resistance (close the nozzle part way)?

_____

(1–4) Analyze the analogy of the bottle to an electric circuit.

1. What does the "push" you made represent?
   _____

2. What does the nozzle represent?
   _____

3. What does the water coming out of the nozzle represent?
   _____

4. Explain this analogy in your own words.
   _____
   _____
   _____
   _____

Stumper's Corner ✏

1. _____
   _____

2. _____
   _____

Thinking About

Date:

The Activity:
Procedure and Observations

What happens to the numbers on your solar calculator screen when the solar batteries are covered up?

_____

_____

Remove the covering over the solar batteries. What happens?

_____

_____

After five minutes, read the thermometers. Record the temperature inside each box as you take them.

Box 1	Box 2
1st temp. _____	1st temp. _____
2nd temp. _____	2nd temp. _____
3rd temp. _____	3rd temp. _____
4th temp. _____	4th temp. _____

Look carefully at the thermometer readings from each box. Subtract the first temperature from the last temperature in Box 1.

_____

Subtract the first temperature from the last temperature in Box 2.

_____

Which box got the hottest? _____

Dig Deeper

What Did You Learn ?

1. Name an invisible wave that comes to the earth from the sun, has a wavelength longer than red, and can be felt as heat when it is absorbed by an object. _____

2. When an object absorbs light, what energy change takes place? _____

3. Give at least two ways that solar power can be used.
   1. _____   2. _____

4. How can you recharge a solar battery? _____

5. Does sunscreen lotion help prevent ultraviolet waves from being absorbed by your skin? _____

6. What are some beneficial uses of ultraviolet and infrared light? _____ _____

7. What kind of electromagnetic waves cause a sunburn, are known as "black light," and cause fluorescent paints to glow? _____

8. Which kind of electromagnetic wave is considered most dangerous — one with a very long wavelength or one with a very short wavelength? _____

9. Can electromagnetic waves travel through empty space? _____

10. When do infrared waves change into heat energy? _____

Narrative: Nonrenewable Conditions for Nonrenewable Fuels

Discussion: After the questions have been discussed, you may choose one or more to answer like a Dig Deeper project.

Which of the two explanations for how the fish became a fossil do you think is most logical? Why do you think so?
_____
_____
_____
_____
_____

Conserving and saving our Nonrenewable fuels is becoming more and more important. What are some of the ways we can all conserve energy? Write about one of these ways.
_____
_____
_____
_____
_____

Finding alternative sources of Nonrenewable fuels is also becoming more and more important. What are some of the alternative energy sources scientists and engineers are investigating? Write about one of these sources.
_____
_____
_____
_____

Stumper's Corner

1. _____
   _____

2. _____
   _____

Date:

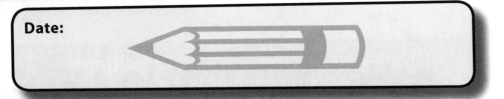

The Activity:
Procedure and Observations

Put an item on the hook. Start small. Blow on each other's windmills with a hair dryer to see if it will lift the item. If your windmill doesn't lift the item, make sure the thread isn't slipping. Your goal will be to lift the item from the floor to the table.

Record the items you were able to lift. Tell if you could lift them completely or just part of the way. Mark if you could not lift it at all. Weigh each item or rank them from lightest to heaviest.

Complete the chart as you do the activity.

Item	Able to lift how high?	Not able to lift	Weight or rank
1			
2			
3			
4			
5			
6			

Dig Deeper

What Did You Learn ?

1. What kind of energy is used by windmills? _____

2. AC electricity is produced from what piece of equipment?
   _____

3. DC electricity is produced from what kind of objects?
   _____

4. What can be done to provide electricity on a wind farm when the wind isn't blowing?
   _____

5. Why are wind farms not a good idea everywhere?
   _____

6. Name some renewable energy sources.
   _____

7. Name some nonrenewable energy sources.
   _____

8. Do all electric generators have moving parts? _____

9. Name at least four ways that electric generators can be turned to produce electricity? (Don't count turbines, because something has to turn the turbines.)
   1. _____   2. _____
   3. _____   4. _____

Stumper's Corner

1. _____
   _____

2. _____
   _____

Date:

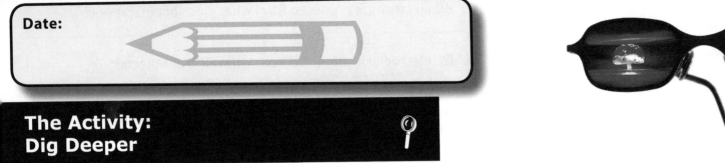

The Activity:
Dig Deeper

Choose any character in this story and do some more research about him or her. Think of a creative way to tell about his or her life and what he or she did.

_____

_____

_____

_____

_____

What are some of the peacetime uses of nuclear energy today?

_____

_____

_____

_____

_____

_____

_____

_____

1. What did Lise and her nephew think they had figured out about what was happening when uranium was bombarded by neutrons?

   _____

   _____

2. Were Lise and her nephew looking for a way to build a new kind of weapon from uranium?

   _____

   _____

Stumper's Corner ✏

1. _____

   _____

2. _____

   _____

Pinwheel Pattern

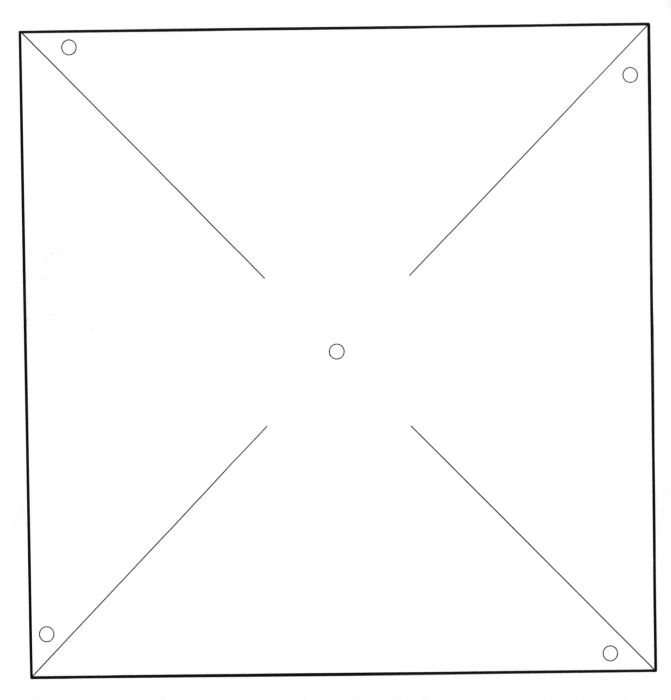

Additional Notes

An exciting 3rd to 6th grade science curriculum!

Finally, a way to study science that your kids will love. Learn science basics like physics and chemistry while you have lots of fun with this activity-based series. Includes activities related to:

- friction
- speed
- inertia
- speed
- lift
- mass
- solar power
- gravity
- energy
- force
- density
- wind energy
- periodic table
- chemical reaction
- acids
- water
- heat

Important scientific terms and concepts are introduced in an engaging series of investigative lessons. Designed to fit into any education program, this informative series offers the best in science education and biblical reinforcement.

11 x 8.5 • Paper • Full Color • 88 pgs.
Retail: $12.99 U.S.
ISBN-13: 978-0-89051-539-6

Forces and Motion - Teacher's Guide
11 x 8.5 • Paper • 48 pg.
Retail: $4.99 U.S.
ISBN-13: 978-0-89051-541-9

Forces and Motion - Student Journal
11 x 8.5 • Paper • 48 pg.
Retail: $4.99 U.S.
ISBN-13: 978-0-89051-540-2

11 x 8.5 • Paper • Full Color • 88 pages
Retail: $12.99 U.S.
ISBN-13: 978-0-89051-560-0

11 x 8.5 • Paper • Full Color • 88 pg.
Retail: $12.99 U.S.
ISBN-13: 978-0-89051-570-9

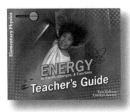

Energy - Teacher's Guide
11 x 8.5 • Paper • 48 pg.
Retail: $4.99 U.S.
ISBN-13: 978-0-89051-572-3

Energy - Student Journal
11 x 8.5 • Paper • 48 pg.
Retail: $4.99 U.S.
ISBN-13: 978-0-89051-571-6

Matter - Teacher's Guide
11 x 8.5 • Paper • 48 pg.
Retail: $4.99 U.S.
ISBN-13: 978-0-89051-561-7

Matter - Student Journal
11 x 8.5 • Paper • 48 pg.
Retail: $4.99 U.S.
ISBN-13: 978-0-89051-559-4